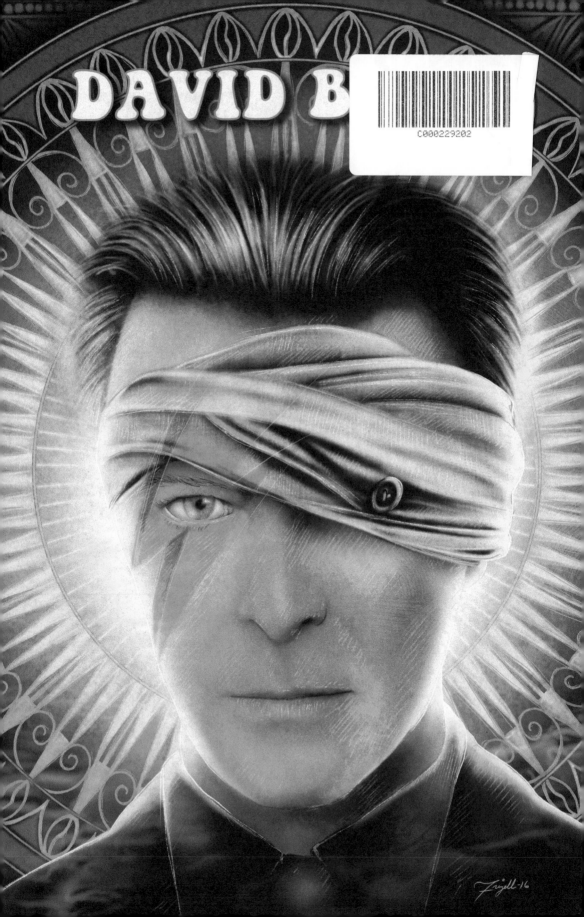

DAVID BOWIE HAS BEEN ONE OF MUSIC'S GREATEST *INNOVATORS.* HIS ABILITY TO REWORK NOT ONLY HIS IMAGE BUT HIS SOUND TOO HAS MADE HIM A LEGEND OF THE BUSINESS.

A MAN NEVER HAPPY TO SETTLE WITH ONE SOUND OR STYLE, HE IS ALWAYS DEVELOPING SOMETHING NEW.

HIS FATHER *HAYWARD JONES* WAS A SMALL TIME CLUB OWNER WHO ALSO WORKED IN AN ORPHANAGE.

AT A YOUNG AGE DAVID'S OLDER BROTHER *TERRY* INTRODUCED DAVID TO ALL TYPES OF MUSIC.

SADLY
TERRY DEVELOPED
SCHIZOPHRENIA.
HE SPENT THE
REST OF HIS LIFE
IN HOSPITAL.

DAVID WAS
EIGHT YEARS OLD
WHEN HE SAW
LITTLE RICHARD
IN A MOVIE AND
THERE AND
THEN HE DECIDED
HE WANTED TO BE A
SAXOPHONE PLAYER.

HIS FATHER BOUGHT HIM A
WHITE PLASTIC SAXOPHONE. HE TOLD
ANYONE THAT WOULD LISTEN
TO HIM THAT ONE DAY HE
WOULD BE IN LITTLE RICHARD'S BAND.

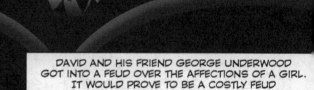

DAVID AND HIS FRIEND GEORGE UNDERWOOD
GOT INTO A FEUD OVER THE AFFECTIONS OF A GIRL.
IT WOULD PROVE TO BE A COSTLY FEUD
FOR THE YOUNG MAN.

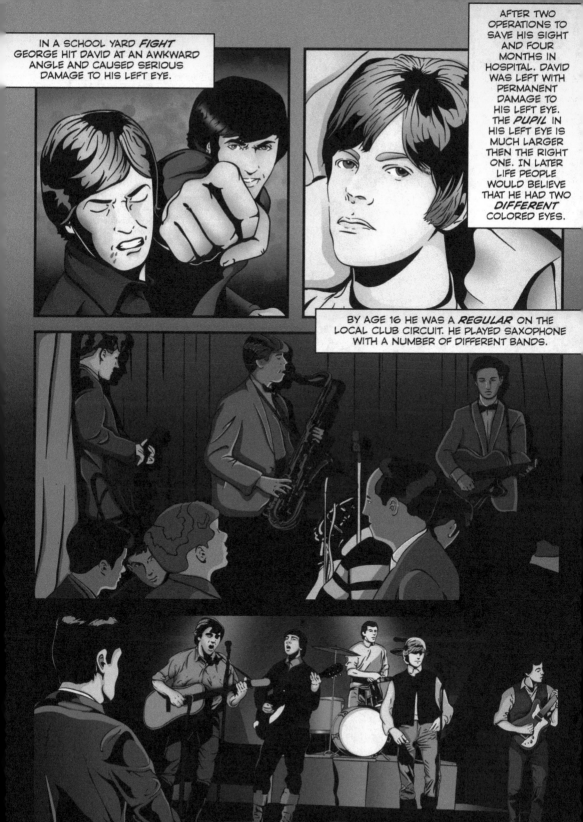

IN A SCHOOL YARD *FIGHT* GEORGE HIT DAVID AT AN AWKWARD ANGLE AND CAUSED SERIOUS DAMAGE TO HIS LEFT EYE.

AFTER TWO OPERATIONS TO SAVE HIS SIGHT AND FOUR MONTHS IN HOSPITAL. DAVID WAS LEFT WITH PERMANENT DAMAGE TO HIS LEFT EYE. THE *PUPIL* IN HIS LEFT EYE IS MUCH LARGER THEN THE RIGHT ONE. IN LATER LIFE PEOPLE WOULD BELIEVE THAT HE HAD TWO *DIFFERENT* COLORED EYES.

BY AGE 16 HE WAS A *REGULAR* ON THE LOCAL CLUB CIRCUIT. HE PLAYED SAXOPHONE WITH A NUMBER OF DIFFERENT BANDS.

HE AUDITIONED FOR *DECCA RECORDS* BUT LIKE THE BEATLES AND THE ROLLING STONES BEFORE HIM WAS TURNED DOWN.

DAVID FIRST
STEPS TOWARDS
SUCCESS CAME
WITH HIS BAND
*DAVIE JONES AND
THE KING BEES*
WHEN THEY RELEASED
THE SINGLE
LIZA JANE.

HE THEN JOINED THE BAND *THE
MANISH BOYS* AND IN LATE 1964
THEY STAGED A PUBLICITY STUNT.
DAVID CREATED THE SOCIETY
FOR THE PREVENTION OF CRUELTY
TO LONG-HAIRED MEN.

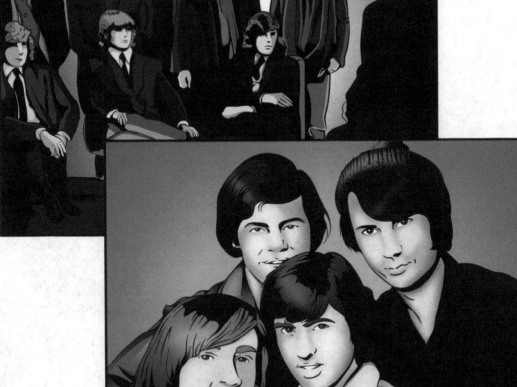

DAVID TOOK A BLOW TO HIS EGO WHEN *ANOTHER*
DAVID JONES BECAME FAMOUS BEFORE HIM. DAVIE JONES FROM
THE MONKEES TOOK THE CHARTS BY STORM. DAVID DECIDED
TO CHANGE HIS SURNAME TO *BOWIE* AFTER THE HUNTING KNIFE.

IN JUNE 1967 HE RELEASED HIS FIRST ALBUM. THE ALBUM GOT GOOD REVIEWS FROM CRITICS BUT DIDN'T SELL VERY WELL.

WITH THE FAILURE OF HIS FIRST ALBUM DAVID GOT INVOLVED IN *THEATRE*. HE AUDITIONED FOR MANY FILM ROLES AND STUDIED TO BECOME A MIME.

HE GOT A JOB IN A BBC TELEPLAY AND SOON FELL IN LOVE WITH ONE OF THE ACTRESSES ON THE SHOW *HERMIONE FARTHINGALE*.

THEIR ROMANCE DIDN'T LAST HOWEVER, HERMIONE LEFT DAVID FOR ANOTHER MAN.

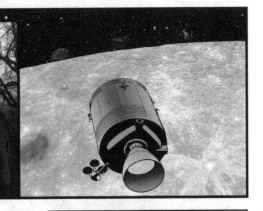

IN 1968 NASA PUT A MAN INTO ORBIT AROUND THE MOON.

THIS EVENT COUPLED WITH HIS BREAK UP WITH HERMIONE INSPIRED HIM TO WRITE A SONG ABOUT A SPACEMAN THAT CUTS OFF COMMUNICATION WITH EARTH. *SPACE ODDITY* WAS WRITTEN WITH JOHN HUTCHINSON IN DAVID'S TINY BEDROOM.

PHILIPS RECORDS RELEASED THE SONG TO CASH IN ON THE EXCITEMENT OF THE APOLLO 11 MISSION.

THE BBC PLAYED THE SONG DURING THEIR COVERAGE OF THE MOON LANDING.

IT WAS SOON AFTER THIS THAT DAVID MET *ANGELA BARNETT.* SHE HAD BEEN DATING A MUSIC EXECUTIVE FROM MERCURY RECORDS WHEN THEY MET.

DAVID GOT A GREAT BOOST WHEN A SONG FROM HIS FIRST EP WAS GIVEN AN AWARD FOR BEST PRODUCED RECORD AT THE MALTA INTERNATIONAL SONG FESTIVAL.

HIS HAPPINESS WAS SHORT-LIVED HOWEVER WHEN HE RETURNED HOME TO FIND HIS FATHER WAS VERY *SICK*. HE DID LIVE LONG ENOUGH TO LEARN OF HIS SON'S SUCCESS IN THE SONG FESTIVAL.

I ALWAYS *KNEW* YOU WOULD SUCCEED IN THE END.

HE DIED TWO DAYS LATER FROM PNEUMONIA.

STILL GRIEVING OVER HIS FATHER'S DEATH DAVID WENT ON THE ROAD WITH THE BAND *HUMBLE PIE*. HE OPENED FOR THE BAND BUT THE AUDIENCE HAD COME FOR A ROCK SHOW AND DAVID'S ACOUSTIC SETS DIDN'T GO OVER WELL WITH THE AUDIENCE.

HE DECIDED TO GO BACK TO A ROCK BASED FORMAT AFTER THIS AND FORMED A NEW BAND CALLED *HYPE*. THE AUDIENCE DIDN'T REALLY WARM TO THE BAND BUT BOWIE WAS INSPIRED. HE BEGAN TO TOY WITH THE IDEA OF CREATING A *PERSONA*.

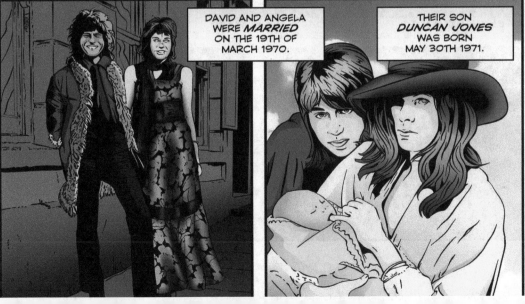

DAVID AND ANGELA WERE *MARRIED* ON THE 19TH OF MARCH 1970.

THEIR SON *DUNCAN JONES* WAS BORN MAY 30TH 1971.

LATER THAT YEAR
DAVID WENT TO NEW YORK
WHERE HE WAS INTRODUCED
TO *ANDY WARHOL*.

HIS FIRST TASTE
OF AMERICAN
SUCCESS CAME
WITH THE SINGLE
CHANGES BUT
DAVID'S NEXT PROJECT
WAS TO CHANGE
EVERYTHING FOR HIM.

IN 1972 DAVID RECREATED HIMSELF AS *ZIGGY STARDUST*.
HE BLURRED THE LINES BETWEEN HIMSELF AND HIS CREATION.
IT WAS HARD TO TELL WHERE DAVID ENDED AND ZIGGY STARTED.
BACKED BY THE SPIDERS FROM MARS DAVID SET OUT TO CONQUER AMERICA.

THEIR FIRST ALBUM *THE RISE AND FALL
OF ZIGGY STARDUST AND THE SPIDERS FROM MARS*
STAYED IN THE CHARTS FOR OVER A YEAR.

IN SEPTEMBER
THE BAND SOLD OUT
CARNEGIE HALL IN
THEIR FIRST AMERICAN
PERFORMANCE. THEY
FOLLOWED THIS UP
WITH A SELL OUT TOUR
OF THE STATES.

LOU REED-TRANSFORMER

HE RETURNED TO ENGLAND TRIUMPHANT. HE THEN SET ABOUT TO PRODUCE LOU REED'S ALBUM *TRANSFORMER*. THE SONG *WALK ON THE WILD SIDE* WOULD BECOME LOU'S BIGGEST HIT.

IN 1973 HE SET ABOUT A WORLD TOUR AND RECORDED HIS NEXT ALBUM *ALADDIN SANE*. IT BECAME THE BEST SELLING ALBUM OF THAT YEAR.

BUT THE STRAIN WAS STARTING TO TAKE IT'S *TOLE* ON HIM. HE SUFFERED FROM BOUTS OF EXHAUSTION. UNDER THIS STRAIN AND A SOURING RELATIONSHIP WITH HIS RECORD COMPANY RCA DAVID DECIDED HE NEEDED A BREAK.

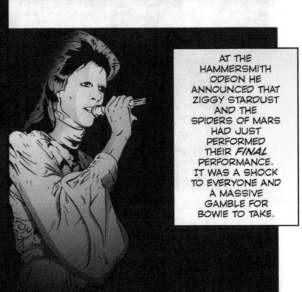

AT THE HAMMERSMITH ODEON HE ANNOUNCED THAT ZIGGY STARDUST AND THE SPIDERS OF MARS HAD JUST PERFORMED THEIR *FINAL* PERFORMANCE. IT WAS A SHOCK TO EVERYONE AND A MASSIVE GAMBLE FOR BOWIE TO TAKE.

DAVID WENT TO ROME FOR A LONG HOLIDAY AND THEN SET ABOUT HIS NEXT PROJECT, A ROCK OPERA BASED ON GEORGE ORWELL'S NOVEL *1984*. HE COULD NOT SECURE THE RIGHTS TO THE BOOK HOWEVER AND THE PROJECT WAS SHELVED. BOWIE WAS ALSO BROKE. HIS MANAGEMENT COMPANY WERE SPENDING HIS MONEY TO FINANCE OTHER BANDS WITHOUT HIS PERMISSION.

WITH MONEY TROUBLES HEAVY ON HIS MIND HE WENT INTO THE STUDIO TO RECORD *DIAMOND DOGS*. THE ALBUM WAS MUCH DARKER THEN HIS PREVIOUS WORK.

FOR THE *DIAMOND DOGS TOUR* DAVID HAD HUGE ELABORATE SETS BUILT. IT COST HALF A MILLION DOLLARS TO BUILD. THE TOUR WAS A MASSIVE SUCCESS, NO ONE HAD EVER SEEN A ROCK CONCERT OF THAT SCALE BEFORE. UNFORTUNATELY THE COST OF STAGING THE TOUR WAS HIGH AND DAVID LOST MONEY ON THE PROJECT.

HALFWAY THROUGH THE TOUR UNDER THE ADVISEMENT OF HIS NEW FRIEND JOHN LENNON HE SCRAPPED THE ELABORATE SETS AND STARTED TO PLAY MORE SONGS FROM HIS NEW ALBUM AND THE FOCUS MOVED TOWARDS SOUL.

THIS DRAMATIC CHANGE PUSHED HIM FURTHER INTO DEBT. AFTER THE TOUR HE WORKED WITH JOHN LENNON ON A NEW SONG CALLED *FAME*. IT BECAME A HUGE HIT.

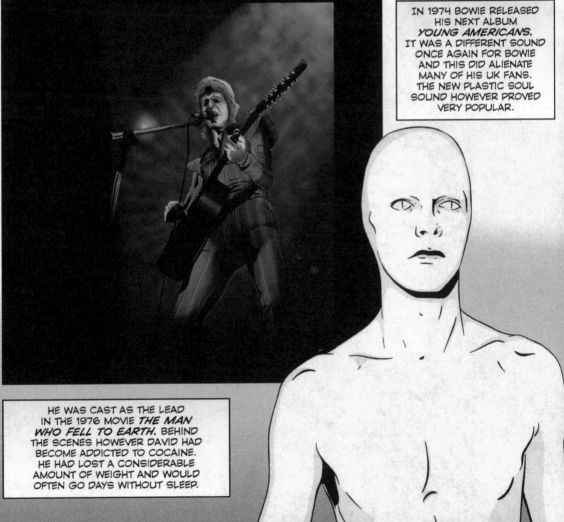

IN 1974 BOWIE RELEASED HIS NEXT ALBUM *YOUNG AMERICANS*. IT WAS A DIFFERENT SOUND ONCE AGAIN FOR BOWIE AND THIS DID ALIENATE MANY OF HIS UK FANS. THE NEW PLASTIC SOUL SOUND HOWEVER PROVED VERY POPULAR.

HE WAS CAST AS THE LEAD IN THE 1976 MOVIE *THE MAN WHO FELL TO EARTH*. BEHIND THE SCENES HOWEVER DAVID HAD BECOME ADDICTED TO COCAINE. HE HAD LOST A CONSIDERABLE AMOUNT OF WEIGHT AND WOULD OFTEN GO DAYS WITHOUT SLEEP.

IN 1976 HE EMBARKED ON A WORLD TOUR. IT WAS A VERY STRANGE TOUR HEAVILY INFLUENCED BY *SURREALISM.*

AT THE LOS ANGELES CONCERT HIS GOOD FRIEND *IGGY POP* STILL IN RECOVERY FOR HEROIN ADDICTION JOINED DAVID ON THE TOUR.

IN MARCH 1976 DAVID AND IGGY WERE ARRESTED IN NEW YORK AND WERE CHARGED WITH THE POSSESSION OF MARIJUANA. THE CHARGES WERE HOWEVER LATER DROPPED.

IN MAY OF THAT YEAR A GREATEST HITS ALBUM OF BOWIE'S WORK WAS RELEASED. IT WAS ENTITLED *CHANGESONEBOWIE.* IT WAS A HUGE SUCCESS AND THIS COUPLED WITH A LARGE SETTLEMENT HE RECEIVED FROM HIS FORMER MANAGEMENT COMPANY HE WAS FINALLY SEEING THE FINANCIAL REWARDS OF ALL HIS HARD WORK.

THE SAME YEAR HE PRODUCED IGGY POP'S ALBUM *THE IDIOT*.
IT WOULD GO ON TO REVIVE IGGY'S CAREER.

DAVID AND
IGGY WERE
STILL HEAVILY
INTO DRUGS
AND COULD
BARELY TAKE
CARE OF
THEMSELVES.
THE PAIR
RELOCATED
TO BERLIN IN
AN ATTEMPT TO
GET CLEAN.

BOWIE WAS
OBSESSED WITH THE
HISTORY OF BERLIN.
IT HAD A PROFOUND
EFFECT ON HIS MUSIC
AND LIFE. HE BEGAN
TO WORK WITH
BRAIN ENO THE
FORMER KEYBOARD
PLAYER FOR *ROXY
MUSIC*. THE PAIR
COLLABORATED AND
WITH BRIAN'S NEW
AMBIENT MUSIC SOUND
THEY CREATED
THREE ALBUMS.

DAVID REFUSED TO PROMOTE
THEIR FIRST ALBUM *LOW*.
INSTEAD HE WENT ON TOUR WITH IGGY
TO PROMOTE HIS ALBUM THE IDIOT.

THE SECOND ALBUM HE WORKED ON WITH BRIAN ENO WAS *HEROES*. HE TOOK A BREAK AFTER THE ALBUM'S RELEASE TO FOCUS ON HIS PERSONAL LIFE.

AFTER HIS WIFE ATTEMPTED SUICIDE DAVID DIVORCED HER AND APPLIED FOR SOLE CUSTODY OF THEIR SON. ANGELA'S ATTEMPTED SUICIDE HAD A PROFOUND EFFECT ON HIM.

IN 1980 DAVID TURNED HIS TALENTS TO BROADWAY AND STARRED IN *THE ELEPHANT MAN*, THE TRAGIC TALE OF JOHN MERRICK.

Sometimes I think my head is so big because it is so full of dreams—

NOW STARRING
DAVID BOWIE
LIMITED ENGAGEMENT!

THE ELEPHANT MAN

David Bowie

scary

monsters

IN SEPTEMBER OF THAT YEAR *SCARY MONSTERS AND SUPER CREEPS* WAS RELEASED. THE SINGLE *ASHES TO ASHES* MARKED A CLOSE TO THE STORY OF MAJOR TOM WHICH STARTED ALL THE WAY BACK WITH *SPACE ODDITY*.

BY THE EARLY EIGHTIES. BOWIE SUCCESS AND FOLLOWING WAS HUGE. HE HAD BECOME ESTABLISHED AS ONE OF THE BIGGEST NAMES IN MUSIC. HE SET ABOUT A STADIUM TOUR.

THE STADIUM TOUR TURNED OUT TO BE A MISTAKE FOR BOWIE, HE HATED IT. HE DECIDED TO TAKE A BREAK AFTER THE TOUR AND KEPT A LOW PROFILE. HE FOCUSED INSTEAD ON HIS FAMILY.

HE STARTED TO WORK ON MOVIES, HE STARRED IN *MERRY CHRISTMAS MR. LAWRENCE* THE STORY OF A P.O.W. CAMP IN WORLD WAR TWO.

AND AS AN AGING VAMPIRE IN *THE HUNGER* ALONG WITH SUSAN SARANDON.

IN 1983 BOWIE SIGNED A CONTRACT WITH EMI AND WAS REPORTED TO HAVE GOTTEN AN ADVANCE OF 17 MILLION DOLLARS.

HIS VIDEOS WENT INTO HEAVY ROTATION ON THE NEW MUSIC CHANNEL *MTV*.

HE THEN SET OUT ON THE *SERIOUS MOONLIGHT WORLD TOUR*. HE WENT TO 57 CITIES IN 15 DIFFERENT COUNTRIES. THE TOUR SOLD OUT IN A MATTER OF HOURS.

HE APPEARED ON THE COVERS OF *ROLLING STONE* AND TIME MAGAZINES. THE SUCCESS OF THE SINGLE *LET'S DANCE* TURNED DAVID INTO A MAINSTREAM POP STAR.

HE RELEASED *TONIGHT* IN 1984. IT SOLD WELL BUT IT FAILED TO IMPRESS THE CRITICS. IT CONSISTED MOSTLY OF OLD SONGS BUT DESPITE THE DISAPPOINTING REVIEWS DAVID WAS NEVER MORE SUCCESSFUL. BUT DAVID HAD NEVER BEEN MORE LESS INSPIRED IN HIS CAREER, HE CONSIDERED GIVING UP MUSIC ALL TOGETHER.

IN 1985 AFTER MANY FAILED ATTEMPTS DAVID'S BROTHER *TERRY* COMMITTED SUICIDE. DAVID DID NOT ATTEND THE FUNERAL FOR FEAR OF TURNING IT INTO A MEDIA SPECTACLE.

THE SECOND HALF OF THE EIGHTIES WAS A LOW POINT FOR DAVID CREATIVELY. HIS *GLASS SPIDER TOUR* WAS THE MOST SUCCESSFUL TOUR TO DATE BUT HE FELT THAT HE WAS SUFFERING AS AN ARTIST.

HE FORMED A NEW BAND CALLED *TIME MACHINE*. THE BAND ALIENATED MANY OF DAVID'S FANS AND DIVIDED CRITICS. IT DID HOWEVER HELP TO REVIVE DAVID'S LOVE OF MUSIC.

HE ANNOUNCED AT THE START OF THE *SOUND AND VISION TOUR* THAT IT WOULD BE THE LAST TIME HE WOULD SING ANY OF HIS HITS IN CONCERT. HE WAS DETERMINED TO WIPE THE SLATE CLEAN AND START AFRESH AS THE EIGHTIES ENDED.

THE NINETIES SAW A CHANGE IN DAVID'S *ROLE* IN MUSIC. HIS MUSIC HAD HELPED TO INSPIRE MANY OF THE BANDS THAT EMERGED IN THE NINETIES.

IN 1992 HE MARRIED *IMAN ABDULMAJID.*

HE RELEASED A NEW ALBUM CALLED *BLACK TIE, WHITE NOISE.*

DAVID BOWIE

BLACK TIE WHITE NOISE

HE FOUND HIMSELF IN HIGH DEMAND WITH NEW *START UP* RECORD LABELS WHO PAID HIM CONSIDERABLE AMOUNTS TO WORK WITH THEM.

HE REUNITED WITH BRIAN ENO TO WORK ON THE ALBUM *OUTSIDE*.

HE SET OUT ON A TOUR WITH *NINE INCH NAILS*. THIS TOUR REINVIGORATED HIM AND HE SET ABOUT RECORDING HIS NEXT ALBUM *EARTHLING*.

WITH THE SUCCESS OF *EARTHLING* DAVID WAS ONCE AGAIN BACK ON TOP.

HE CELEBRATED HIS *50TH BIRTHDAY* WITH A CONCERT IN MADISON SQUARE GARDEN. HE WAS JOINED BY SONIC YOUTH, FOO FIGHTERS, BILLY CORGAN AND HIS GOOD FRIEND LOU REED.

DAVID'S OUTPUT CONTINUES WELL INTO THE 00'S. IN 2004 HE WAS HIT WITH A SETBACK WHILE PERFORMING IN GERMANY. HE SUFFERED CHEST PAINS AND WAS DIAGNOSED WITH AN ACUTELY BLOCKED CORONARY ARTERY WHICH REQUIRED SURGERY.

FOLLOWING THE HEART ATTACK DAVID REDUCED HIS WORK LOAD BUT HE STILL CONTINUED TO COLLABORATE WITH BANDS SUCH AS *ARCADE FIRE* AND WORKED ON SOUNDTRACKS FOR SEVERAL FILMS.

IN 2006 HE WAS AWARDED THE GRAMMY *LIFETIME ACHIEVEMENT AWARD.*

The Next Day

ON HIS 66TH BIRTHDAY HE RELEASED *THE NEXT DAY.* IT HAS GONE ON TO BE ONE OF DAVID'S MOST WELL RECEIVED ALBUMS TO DATE.

FOR OVER THIRTY YEARS DAVID BOWIE HAS BEEN A LEADING INNOVATOR IN MUSIC. HIS ABILITY TO CONSTANTLY CHANGE HIS STYLE AND SOUND HAS GUARANTEED HIM A PLACE IN MUSIC HISTORY.

OKAY... LET'S TRY IT AGAIN. IT'S IMPORTANT I GET IT RIGHT.

HE GROANED IN HIMSELF AND CRIED IN A LOUD VOICE, "LAZARUS, COME FORTH!"

AND HE WHO HAD DIED CAME OUT BOUND HAND AND FOOT WITH GRAVECLOTHES, AND HIS FACE WAS WRAPPED WITH A CLOTH.

JESUS SAID TO THEM,

"LOOSE HIM...

AND LET HIM GO."

DAVID BOWIE WAS LAID TO REST IN A PRIVATE CEREMONY SURROUNDED BY THOSE HE LOVED.

HIS MUSIC, HOWEVER, LIVES ON.

"THE HIPPIES WANTED PEACE AND LOVE. WE WANTED *FERRARIS, BLONDES, AND SWITCHBLADES.*"

alice cooper

sskrrrtch!

ARE YOU READY TO DO SOMETHING REALLY *SCARY?*

Fsstp

OR IS IT *TOO* SCARY FOR YOU?

DO YOU WANNA RUN HOME TO YOUR MOMMIES?

KNOCK IT *OFF*, RHIANNON.

YEAH, JUST 'CUZ YOU'RE THE OLDEST DOESN'T MEAN YOU HAVE TO BE A JERK.

UH...DO WE *HAFTA* DO THITH?

YES, DREW, WE DO. YOU KNOW WHY.

JON...SUZE... I'M NOT BEING A JERK, I'M JUST TRYING TO HAVE A LITTLE FUN.

JULY 2014: PHOENIX, ARIZONA

I THOUGHT YOU THAID THIS WATH THERIOUTH.

IT *IS* SERIOUS! I...FINE...SORRY!

DO YOU REALLY THINK WE'LL MAKE CONTACT?

WE *HAVE* TO. WE CAN'T STOP HIM ALONE.

WELL, THIS IS ALL *DREW'S* FAULT! IF HE HADN'T SUMMONED HIM –

TAKE THAT *BACKTH!* IT'TH *NOT* MY FAULT!

DREW! *CALM DOWN!*

HAHAHA! WHAT'A'YA GONNA *DO?* BRING IT, LITTLE MAN!

THAT'S ENOUGH! WE HAVE TO DO THIS *NOW!* TIME'S RUNNING OUT! IT'LL BE MIDNIGHT SOON, AND THEN WE'LL BE TOO LATE!

SUZE IS RIGHT. LET'S GET TO IT.

NO CHEATING! IT HAS TO MOVE ON ITS OWN; OTHERWISE, STEVEN WILL NEVER SPEAK TO US!

RIGHT. LET'TH *DO IT!*

"RHIANNON, ARE YOU MEANING TO CONTACT ALICE COOPER THE *BAND* OR ALICE COOPER THE *MAN?*"

"WHAT'S THE DIFFERENCE?"

I READ SOMEWHERE THAT SPIRIT BOARDS ARE JUST VESTIGIAL REMAINS OF PRIMITIVE BELIEF SYSTEMS.

BUT, SUZE... THIS IS HOW VINCENT FURNIER CHANNELED STEVEN AND CHOSE THE NAME *ALICE COOPER!*

NO, THAT'S NOT TRUE. THAT'S JUST ANOTHER *URBAN LEGEND* THAT SURROUNDS THE NAME, THE MAN, AND THE BAND!

"THERE'S A HUGE DIFFERENCE! ALICE COOPER THE *BAND* FEATURED DENNIS DUNAWAY, MICHAEL BRUCE, GLEN BUXTON, AND NEAL SMITH IN ADDITION TO VINCENT FURNIER. WHEN THEY BROKE UP IN 1975, FURNIER CHANGED HIS LEGAL NAME TO ALICE COOPER."

I THINK THEY'RE ONE AND THE SAME.

RIGHT! THEY *ARE!* THAT'S WHAT I'M TRYING TO TELL YOU!

LIKE...LIKE GOD AND HIS SON AND THE HOLY GHOST! THEY'RE ALL KINDA THE SAME...*DEITY*...PERSON.

I CAN'T BELIEVE YOU WENT THERE.

LOOK, RHIA, I KNOW YOU THINK THIS IS GONNA HELP, BUT ALICE COOPER IS AN *IDEA* THAT SPURRED CREATIVITY IN VINCENT FURNIER AND HIS BANDMATES AND CREATED A TYPE OF ROCK AND ROLL THAT INFLUENCED MANY OTHERS. BUT THE ALICE COOPER...STEVEN... YOU'RE HOPING TO *SUMMON* ISN'T REAL.

BUT IDEAS ARE POWERFUL, AND POWERFUL IDEAS TAKE ON A LIFE OF THEIR *OWN,* RIGHT?

I...I GUESS. SURE. WHATEV. I GIVE UP.

SO PUT YOUR HAND ON THE POINTER-THING —

PLANCHETTE.

— PLANCHETTE AND *SHUT UP!* DREW!

WHAT?

REMEMBER TO WRITE DOWN EVERYTHING YOU SEE AND HEAR, DREW. YOU'RE "THE DOCUMENTER." AND NO MORE DRAWING THOSE SYMBOLS!

'KAY.

OKAY. LIKE I SAID EARLIER... NO CHEATING!

REMEMBER: THIS IS NOT A GAME. THE OUIJA IS A SERIOUS TOOL USED TO MANIPULATE THE ETHEREAL ENERGIES WE EMIT INTO THE WORLD AROUND US. A POWERFUL MAGIC THAT BINDS US ALL TO EACH OTHER.

LIKE "MIDICHLORIANS." POWERFUL JEDI, YES. POWERFUL, HE IS. HMMM?

≶GIGGLE!≶

"THE FIRST TWO ROWS OF THAT AUDIENCE WERE ALL IN *WHEEL-CHAIRS.* THEY WERE THE ONES WHO TORE THE CHICKEN TO PIECES.

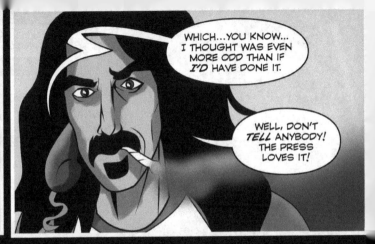

WHICH...YOU KNOW...I THOUGHT WAS EVEN MORE ODD THAN IF *I'D* HAVE DONE IT.

WELL, DON'T *TELL* ANYBODY! THE PRESS LOVES IT!

"THAT CONTROVERSY HAS FOLLOWED COOPER WHEREVER HE GOES. HE REFINED HIS LOOK WHEN HE WENT SOLO IN 1975. EVEN CHANGED HIS NAME LEGALLY FROM VINCENT FURNIER TO ALICE COOPER."

BUT NONE OF THIS IS HELPING. THERE'S SO MUCH TO TALK ABOUT! HIS ALBUMS ARE MOSTLY CONCEPTUAL. HE'S APPEARED ON TELEVISION, TOO...

LIKE WITH THE *MUPPETS!*

"I KNEW I WAS IN TROUBLE."

"MY FAME HAS MADE A TARGET. I'VE STRUGGLED AGAINST RUMORS..."

...ADDICTION...

...AND EVEN A STINT AWAY FROM HER.

"WE'VE GOT THREE KIDS NOW. THEY ARE CLEARLY MY POWER. AS LONG AS I WEAR THIS BRACELET, I ALWAYS FEEL THEY'RE NEAR ME."

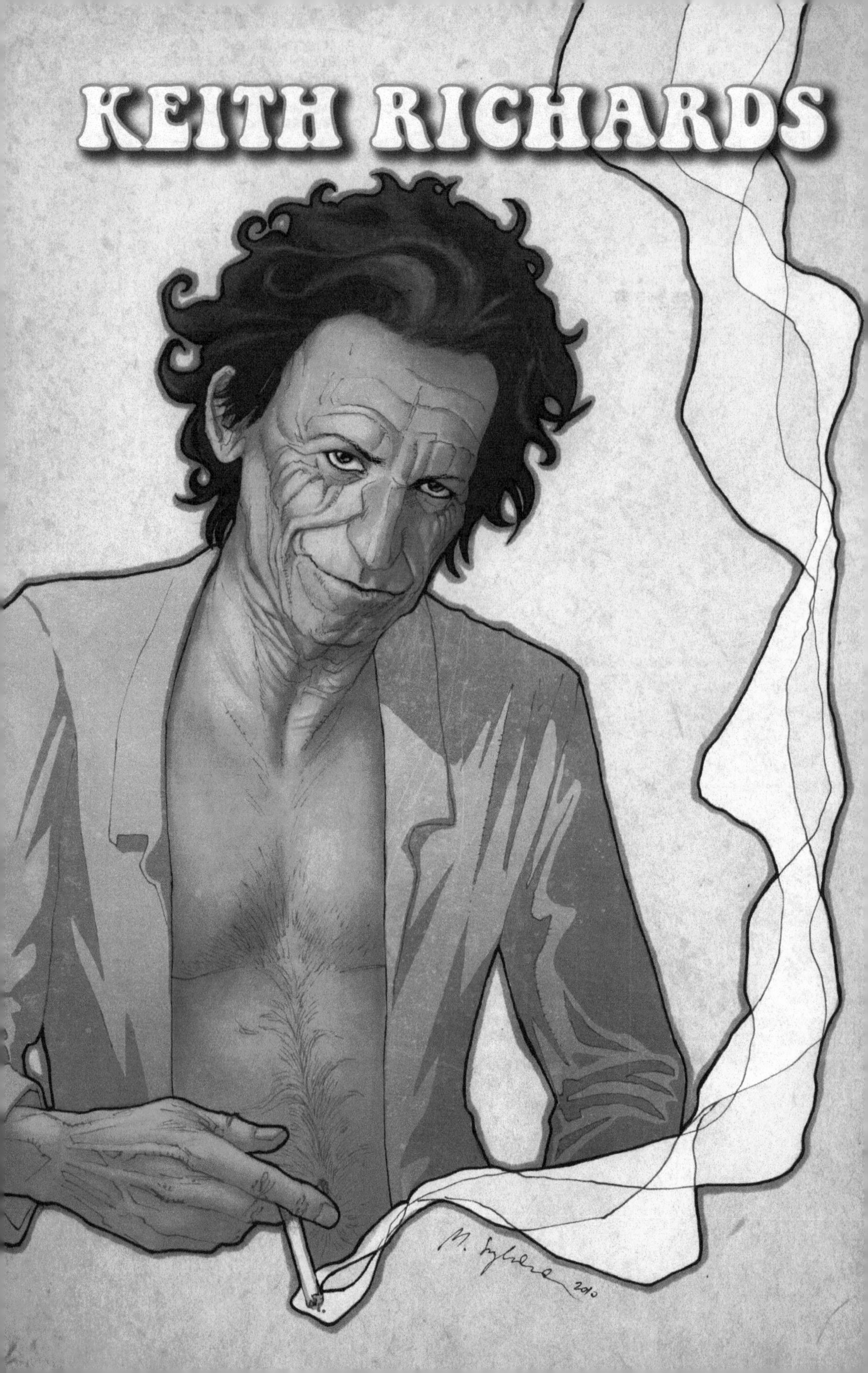
KEITH RICHARDS

MEET KEITH RICHARDS -- GUITAR GOD, HELL-RAISER, JUNKIE-OUTLAW, SONGWRITING LEGEND. HE'S RECORDED MORE THAN 80 ALBUMS. 25 WENT PLATINUM, 14 WENT GOLD. POLICE ON EVERY CONTINENT HAVE CHASED HIM, PRESIDENTS AND ROYALTY HAVE FOUGHT TO MEET HIM. HE DOESN'T JUST PLAY ROCK 'N ROLL -- HE INVENTED IT.

AND AT THIS MOMENT, HE'S DYING.

YES, I'VE BEEN TREPANNED.*

* A MEDICAL INTERVENTION IN WHICH A HOLE IS DRILLED OR SCRAPED INTO THE SKULL.

HE'S BLEEDING INTO HIS BRAIN AFTER FALLING OFF A TREE BRANCH. OF ALL THE THINGS THAT SHOULD HAVE KILLED HIM, THIS IS THE LEAST LIKELY.

THAT'S QUITE AN INTERESTING EXPERIENCE, ESPECIALLY FOR MY BRAIN SURGEON, WHO SAW MY THOUGHTS FLYING AROUND IN MY BRAIN.

VE GOT PICTURES OF IT
ATE, YEAH. THEY CUT MY
EAD, BRAIN, SKULL OPEN,
ENT IN AND PULLED OUT
E CRAP, AND PUT SOME
IT BACK IN AGAIN.

CRRRRRRR

BUT THAT'S THE WAY IT IS, I MEAN, SHIT, KEITH RICHARDS HAS GOT TO DO EVERYTHING ONCE.

♫ I WAS BORN IN A CROSS-FIRE HURRICANE ... ♪

KEITH WAS A SHY AND ARTISTIC CHILD. ALTHOUGH MICK JAGGER WAS ONE OF HIS SCHOOLMATES THEY WOULDN'T BECOME FRIENDS UNTIL MUCH LATER.

KEITH'S FAMILY SQUEAKED BY IN POST-WAR BRITAIN. MONEY WAS TIGHT AND LUXURY ITEMS - MEAT, MILK OR CANDY - WERE GOVERNMENT RATIONED.

I'LL BE THE COWBOYS AND YOU BE THE INDIANS.

LEAVE ME BE, KEITH.

MY DAD WORKED HIS BUTT OFF IN ORDER TO KEEP THE RENT PAID AND FOOD FOR THE FAMILY.

HE DIDN'T KNOW HOW TO OPEN HIMSELF UP.

SURE, DAD.

AT LEAST MY MOTHER HAD GOOD TASTE IN MUSIC.

♪MAMA MAY HAVE, PAPA MAY HAVE, BUT GOD BLESS THE CHILD THAT'S GOT HIS OWN! ♫

BUT LIFE WAS ABOUT TO GET HARDER.

IN 1954 MY FAMILY MOVED TO THIS FUCKING SOUL-DESTROYING COUNCIL ESTATE ON THE OTHER END OF TOWN. A DISGUSTING CONCRETE JUNGLE OF HORRIBLE NEW HOUSES... BECAUSE HE WOULDN'T TAKE A CHANCE ON ANYTHING...

KEITH'S MOM BOUGHT HIM A GUITAR FOR HIS 15TH BIRTHDAY, ON CREDIT.

MUM! HOW'D YOU DO IT?

NEVER YOU MIND.

KEITH'S DAD WAS LESS SUPPORTIVE.

♫ MY HEARTS BEATIN' RHYTHM AND MY SOUL KEEPS A-SINGIN' THE BLUES! ROLL OVER BEETHOVEN AND TELL - ♪

STOP THAT BLOODY NOISE!!!

KEITH WAS KICKED OUT OF DARTFORD TECH FOR TRUANCY AND TRANSFERRED TO SIDCUP, AN ART COLLEGE.

I FUCKIN' HATED SCHOOL. I'LL LET DICKY TELL YOU ABOUT IT.

DICK "STEEL HAND" TAYLOR OF THE PRETTY THINGS.

KEITH WAS A BIT OF A LAYABOUT AT ART SCHOOL. HIS INTEREST WAS IN PLAYING GUITAR NOTHING ELSE COUNTED.

KEITH'S DEDICATION WAS EPIC. HE PRACTICED 6 TO 8 HOURS A DAY.

TO STAY UP LATE WITH OUR MUSIC ... KEITH AND I WERE ON A PRETTY STEADY DIET OF PEP PILLS. PILLS GIRLS TOOK FOR MENSTRUATION, INHALERS, NOSTRILENE, AND OTHER STUFF.

IN 1961 KEITH BUMPS INTO HIS OLD SCHOOL MATE, MICK JAGGER.

IS THAT THE NEW CHUCK BERRY?

STRAIGHT FROM THE STATES. COME OVER FOR A LISTEN?

MICK JAGGER, AKA HER MAJESTY "BRENDA".

LITTLE SNOT NOSE ME.

ABSOLUTELY!

♫ BEFORE YOU ACCUSE ME TAKE A LOOK AT YOURSELF ♪

MORE THAN HIS MARRIAGES, THIS IS THE RELATIONSHIP THAT WILL DEFINE KEITH'S LIFE.

WITHIN A YEAR, KEITH DROPS OUT OF SIDCUP. HE AND JAGGER FORM....

THE ROLLING STONES

BRIAN JONES,
GUITAR

KEITH RICHARDS,
GUITAR

BILL WYMAN,
BASS

CHARLIE WATTS,
DRUMMER

MICK JAGGER,
VOCALS

Would you let your daughter marry a Rolling Stone?

THEY'RE THE ANTI-BEATLES: SHAGGY, ANGRY AND
SEXUAL. MICK IS THE FACE OF THE BAND, BUT KEITH
IS ITS HEART-AND-SOUL WITH HIS DRIVING R&B
INSPIRED GUITAR RIFFS.

ROCK AND
ROLL: MUSIC FOR
THE NECK
DOWNWARDS.

I DON'T NEED
TO HEAR BILL TO
GO THROUGH A SONG.
I NEED TO HEAR
KEITH ...

YOU HAVE
NO WAY OF NOT
FOLLOWING
HIM.

IN 1965, HE RECORDS 40 SECONDS OF FEVERED GUITAR AND FIVE WORDS IN HIS SLEEP.

C!CK!

KEITH OFTEN SLEEPS WITH HIS GUITAR, IN CASE INSPIRATION STRIKES.

I CAN'T GET NO SATISFACTION... ♪

FOUR WEEKS LATER THE RIFF WOULD ROCKET HIM TO INTERNATIONAL FAME AS "(I CAN'T GET NO) SATISFACTION."

ZZZZZZZZ

SQIK! SQIK! SQIK!

AN AMERICAN MAGAZINE WOULD CALL IT, "FIVE NOTES THAT SHOOK THE WORLD." FUCKIN' RIGHT, YEAH?

IT WAS THE SONG THAT REALLY MADE THE ROLLING STONES... IT HAS A GREAT GUITAR SOUND, WHICH WAS ORIGINAL AT THE TIME.

AW, MICK. AND I DIDN GET YOU NUTHIN'. WRUGH, WRUGH, WRUGH.

POPSTARS AND DRUGS

FAC THAT WILL SHOCK

BULLOCKS.

I'M GOING TO SUE THAT GODDAMN TABLOID. HALF OF IT'S LIES.

WHAT ABOUT THE OTHER HALF?

BAM BAM BAM

HEY, THEY'VE GOT THIS FUNNY SCRAP OF PAPER. LEGAL RUBBISH.

WARRA

KEITH AND MICK ARE ARRESTED ON DRUG CHARGES, THE FIRST OF MANY. KEITH IS SENTENCED TO ONE YEAR, BUT LATER WINS ON APPEAL.

EASY ON HER, MATE!

WHEN WE GOT BUSTED... THAT IS WHEN THE FUN STOPPED. UP UNTIL THEN IT HAD BEEN AS THOUGH LONDON EXISTED IN A BEAUTIFUL SPACE WHERE YOU COULD DO ANYTHING YOU WANTED.

♪ GOODBYE, RUBY TUESDAY ♫
WHO CAN HANG A NAME ON YOU?

FREE PENDING APPEAL, KEITH
HEADS TO MORROCCO WITH BRIAN
JONES AND HIS GIRLFRIEND ANITA.
IT'S A CHANCE TO COOL THEIR
NERVES AND BLOW OFF
SOME STEAM.

LOOK AWAY, MATE,
SHE'S WITH ME.

KEITH!
HELP ME.

ANITA,
WHAT DID
HE DO?!

YOU'RE TRASH,
YOU KNOW THAT?
THE BOTH OF YOU!

SHUT
IT, BRIAN,
OR I WILL.

IT'S
ALRIGHT,
KEITH.

FUCK THIS, KNOB.
I'M TAKING YOU
BACK TO LONDON.

ANITA LEAVES MORROCCO WITH
KEITH. THEY GO ON TO HAVE THREE
CHILDREN TOGETHER, MARLON,
DANDELION, ANGELA AND TARA.

BRIAN'D NEVER
FORGIVE ME FOR
THAT AND I DON'T
BLAME HIM, BUT
HELL, SHIT
HAPPENS.

BRIAN JONES LEAVES
THE STONES IN 1969.
HE DIES OF AN OVERDOSE
A MONTH LATER.

1971-- KEITH MOVES THE VILLA NELLCOTE IN THE SOUTH OF FRANCE TO AVOID ENGLISH TAXES... AND ENGLISH POLICE.

GIMME SHELTER

Oh, a storm is threatening my very life today

THE FUCK IS THE WANKER...

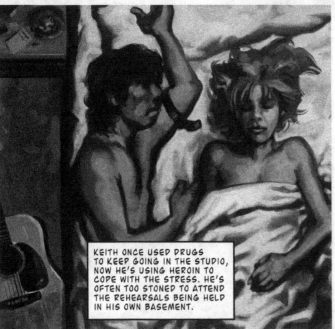

FAME'LL KILL YA. JIMI HENDRIX DIED OF FAME, NOT THE DRUGS. MARK MY WORDS.

KEITH ONCE USED DRUGS TO KEEP GOING IN THE STUDIO, NOW HE'S USING HEROIN TO COPE WITH THE STRESS. HE'S OFTEN TOO STONED TO ATTEND THE REHEARSALS BEING HELD IN HIS OWN BASEMENT.

♫ ALWAYS TOOK CANDY FROM STRANGERS DIDN'T WANT TO GET ME NO TRADE NEVER WANT TO BE LIKE MY PAPA WORKING FOR THE BOSS EV'RY NIGHT AND DAY ♪

QUITTERS

HAPPY WAS SOMETHING I DID BECAUSE I WAS FOR ONE TIME EARLY FOR A SESSION. IT WAS JUST AN AFTERNOON JAM THAT EVERYBODY SAID, "WOW, YEAH, WORK ON IT!"

The Stones' Exil
By Robert Christgau

More than anything e masterpiece is difficu else describe music t weeks and co in its ov

EXILE ON MAINSTREET IS RELEASED AS A SPRAWLING DOUBLE SET. IT'S HERALDED AS THEIR GREATEST WORK TO-DATE.

e, Angie, when will those clouds disappear
(scrawled handwriting) ...iT lead us from here?

DANDELION ANGIE RICHARDS IS BORN IN 1972. HER NAME IS GIVEN TO THE STONES #1 HIT.

SHE'S BEAUTIFUL.

WAH-WAH-WAAAAH!

WAAAAAAAAHHHHH!

IT'S OK, LUV. DADDY'S HERE.

KEITH AND ANITA'S HEROIN USAGE IS SO SEVERE THAT HE SENDS ANGIE TO BE RAISED BY HIS MOTHER.

HE'S ARRESTED TWICE MORE BEFORE THE END OF THE YEAR.

IN THE 1970'S KEITH'S HARD-PARTYING WAYS WERE LEGENDARY.

ROCK CRITIC NICK KENT DESCRIBED KEITH AS "A LORD BYRON FIGURE. HE WAS MAD, BAD AND DANGEROUS TO KNOW."

HE SLOWED DOWN TOURS...

...DELAYED SHOWS...

...EVEN FELL ASLEEP ONSTAGE.

1976. THE STONES TOUR IN SUPPORT OF THEIR ALBUM, BLACK AND BLUE.

I DON'T REGRET NUTHIN'. I EVEN SNORTED MY DEAR OLD DAD'S ASHES ONCE.

"THE HEAT OFF, BECAU IT'S ALL OV THEY REAL DON'T MATT ANYMORE STAND FO ANYTHING.

CAN YOU BELIEVE THIS PRA KEITH.

THE ALBUM GOES MULTI-PLATINUM BUT MICK IS SENSITIVE TO THE REVIEWS. HE AND KEITH GROW APART AS KEITH DISAPPEARS EVEN FURTHER INTO ADDICTION.

IT'S LIKE I'M THE ONLY ONE PULLIN' THIS TRAIN.

BUT ON JUNE 6TH HE GOT A WAKE-UP CALL OF THE CRUELEST KIND. HIS INFANT SON, TARA, WAS DEAD.

FOR THE FIRS TIME, KEITH BEGINS TO QUESTION HIS HEROIN USE. AND ANITA'S.

MY BABY... WAS ANITA USING? I SHOULDA BEEN THERE.

1977 - THE STONES PLAY TWO SURPRISE CONCERTS IN TORONTO WHERE THEY ARE RECORDING THEIR NEW ALBUM. IT CAUSES A SENSATION IN THE CITY.

WHAT'S HER DEAL?

BLIND, I GUESS.

GET HER HOME SAFE. A LOT OF BAD THINGS CAN HAPPEN TO A BLIND GIRL ON THE STREETS.

DIDN'T THINK I HAD THAT IN ME, DO YOU? THERE'S PLENTY YOU DON'T KNOW, MATE.

A FEW NIGHTS LATER KEITH IS BUSTED WITH 22 GRAMS OF HEROIN. HE'S CHARGED WITH POSSESSION FOR THE PURPOSE OF TRAFFICKING.

SEE YOU IN SEVEN YEARS, LOVE.

IT'S WORSE THAN THAT. THE CHARGES CARRIES A SENTENCE OF 7 YEARS TO LIFE.

KEITH ATTENDS REHAB WHILE AWAITING TRIAL. FEW THINK THAT HE CAN CLEAN HIMSELF UP.

ONE MINUTE I'M OPERATING AS A SUPERSTAR AND THE NEXT I'M SHOOTING UP WITH SOME GUYS ON THE LOWER EAST SIDE.

I TOOK DRUGS BECAUSE I WANTED TO HIDE.

KEITH DIDN'T KNOW IT BUT HE HAD AN ALLY.

I'M SORRY TO DISTURB YOU, BUT YOU SHOULD KNOW SOMETHING...

MOVED BY HIS COMPASSION FOR HER, THE BLIND GIRL FROM THE CONCERT SOUGHT OUT THE JUDGE AT HIS HOME AND PLEADED FOR MERCY.

I SENTENCE YOU TO TIME-SERVED AND PROBATION. IN ADDITION YOU WILL NEED TO PLAY TWO CONCERTS... FOR THE BENEFIT OF BLIND CHARITIES.

THE JUDGE DECIDED JUSTICE WOULD BE TO REPAY KEITH IN-KIND.

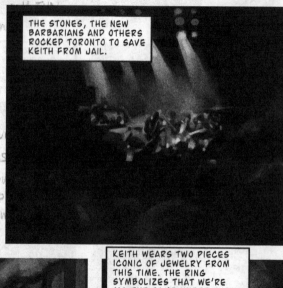

THE STONES, THE NEW BARBARIANS AND OTHERS ROCKED TORONTO TO SAVE KEITH FROM JAIL.

I'M SORRY, LUV.

BUT NOTHING CAN SAVE KEITH AND ANITA. HE'S DETERMINED TO GO STRAIGHT BUT SHE IS UNABLE TO AND THEY SPLIT.

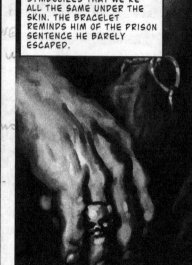

KEITH WEARS TWO PIECES ICONIC OF JEWELRY FROM THIS TIME. THE RING SYMBOLIZES THAT WE'RE ALL THE SAME UNDER THE SKIN. THE BRACELET REMINDS HIM OF THE PRISON SENTENCE HE BARELY ESCAPED.

THE BAND REUNITES TO RECORD THEIR COMEBACK ALBUM, DIRTY WORK.

WHERE'S HER MAJESTY?

UM - MICK'S GOING TO LAY DOWN HIS TRACKS SEPARATE.

WHAT I GOTTA DO, SEND FLOWERS AND CHOCOLATE?

MY POINT WITH DIRTY WORK WAS THAT THIS WAS THE TIME WHEN THE STONES COULD DO SOMETHING. THEY COULD MATURE AND GROW THIS MUSIC UP...

AMID RUMORS THAT THE BAND IS BREAKING UP, MICK REFUSES TO TOUR DIRTY WORK.

KEITH kicked from ban

MICK GOES SOLO!

TO ME, TWENTY FIVE YEARS OF INTEGRITY WE DOWN THE DR WITH WHAT HE DID.

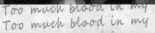

Too much blood in my
Too much blood in my

MICK PUTS OUT SHE'S THE BOSS IN 1985. THEN PRIMITIVE COOL IN 1987.

IT'S THE BEST WORK I'VE EVER DONE. HANDS DOWN.

YOU WANKER ...

YOU CAN'T WAIT FOR MICK TO COME BACK, BABY.

YEAH... MAYBE IT'S TIME.

♪ NOW YOU WANT TO THROW THE DICE YOU ALREADY CRAPPED OUT TWICE ♪

1988 -- KEITH RECORDS TALK IS CHEAP, HIS FIRST SOLO EFFORT. IT'S LAUDED AS "THE FINEST 'ROLLING STONES' ALBUM IN YEARS".

BUT WHAT REALLY HAS TONGUES WAGGING IS KEITH'S UNBRIDLED ATTACKS ON MICK.

YOU WANKER ...

IT'S NO LONGER FUNNY IT'S BIGGER THAN MONEY YOU DON'T MOVE ME ANYMORE

MICK'S AND MY BATTLES ARE NOT EXACTLY AS PERCEIVED...

THEY'RE FAR MORE CONVOLUTED BECAUSE WE'VE KNOWN EACH OTHER OUR WHOLE LIVES.

THEY INVOLVE A LOT OF SUBTLETIES AND INS AND OUTS THAN CAN POSSIBLY BY EXPLAINED.

1989 -- THE ROLLING STONES REUNITE TO PRACTICE BEFORE BEING INDUCTED TO THE ROCK AND ROLL HALL OF FAME.

IT'S ONE OF THE FEW TIMES KEITH AND MICK HAVE BEEN IN THE SAME ROOM SINCE 1985.

WE AIN'T FRIENDS, WE'RE FAMILY.

WE SCREA 'TIL W CLEAR THE A

♪ YOU'RE NOT THE ONLY ONE WITH MIXED EMOTIONS YOU'RE NOT THE ONLY SHIP ADRIFT ON THIS OCEAN ♫

THE REVIEWS ARE BETTER THAN EITHER OF THEIR SOLO EFFORTS. ROCK CRITIC, DAVID SINCLAIR...

KEITH AND MICK COMPOSE MORE THAN 50 SONGS IN FOUR WEEKS. STEEL WHEELS GOES DOUBLE-PLATINUM AND BECOMES THE LARGEST GROSSING TOUR IN HISTORY.

NOT ONLY DID THE ROLLING STONES COME OUT OF THE TRAPS CONSIDERABLY FASTER THAN THE CURRENT WAVE OF MOUTHY YOUNG TURKS, BUT THEY HAVE STAYED THE COURSE IN A WAY THAT SURELY DEFIES BELIEF.

2007 -- KEITH'S MOTHER, DORIS, IS COMING TO THE END OF HER LIFE AT THE AGE OF 91.

BEEP...
BEEP...
BEEP...

DAD, WHY DON'T YOU PLAY FOR HER?

WELL, IF YOU SEE CLOUDS HERE IN MY EYES
IT'S JUST BECAUSE YOU SAY GOOD-BYE
..THOUGH THE SUN IS SHINING, THERE'S NO SUMMER SKIES
STILL IT'S RAINING TEARDROPS FROM MY EYES ♫

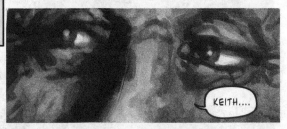

KEITH....

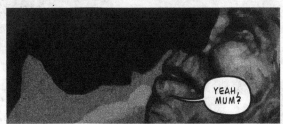

YEAH, MUM?

YOU'RE OUT OF TUNE.

I'LL WORK ON THAT, MUM. I WILL.

DORIS DUPREE RICHARDS, THE ROCK IN KEITH'S LIFE, DIED APRIL 21ST, 2007.

2006 -- KEITH PLAYS CAPTAIN SPARROW'S FATHER IN PIRATES OF THE CARIBBEAN 3.

THIS LARK WAS JOHNNY'S IDEA. A BIT OF FUN, REALLY.

PEOPLE ALWAYS ASK ME, WHEN AM I GOING TO HANG IT UP?

I PLAYED WITH MUDDY WATERS SIX MONTHS BEFORE HE DIED, AND THE CAT WAS JUST AS VITAL AS HE WAS IN HIS YOUTH. I MEAN, WHAT AM I GONNA DO NOW, LEARN TO BE A WELDER?

THAT'S A WRAP!

ROCK N' ROLL...

IT'S A JOB. IT'S A MAN'S JOB, AND IT'S A LIFELONG JOB.

AND IF THERE'S A SUCKER TO EVER PROVE IT, I HOPE TO BE THE SUCKER. IT'S A SIMPLE EQUATION REALLY...

YOU'VE GOT THE SUN, YOU'VE GOT THE MOON, AND YOU'VE GOT THE ROLLING STONES

THE END

His own song, *"Don't Stop 'til You Get Enough,"* even won him his first solo Grammy Award, as well as his first ever American Music Award.

He also had trouble keeping romantic relationships.

It seemed to him that the girls he dated were only there to rescue him from his *desolation*...

But, as successful as *Off the Wall* was and as numerous as his fans were, the loneliness Michael had felt during his adolescence was creeping into his adulthood.

During the production of *Off the Wall*, he felt that he had very few close friends.

...Michael didn't want that, though. He didn't want *anyone* to go through the pain he was feeling.

His loneliness became so difficult to deal with sometimes that he would walk the streets of his neighborhood at night looking for someone to talk to...

Someone who didn't know who he was...

...And who *also* wanted a friend.

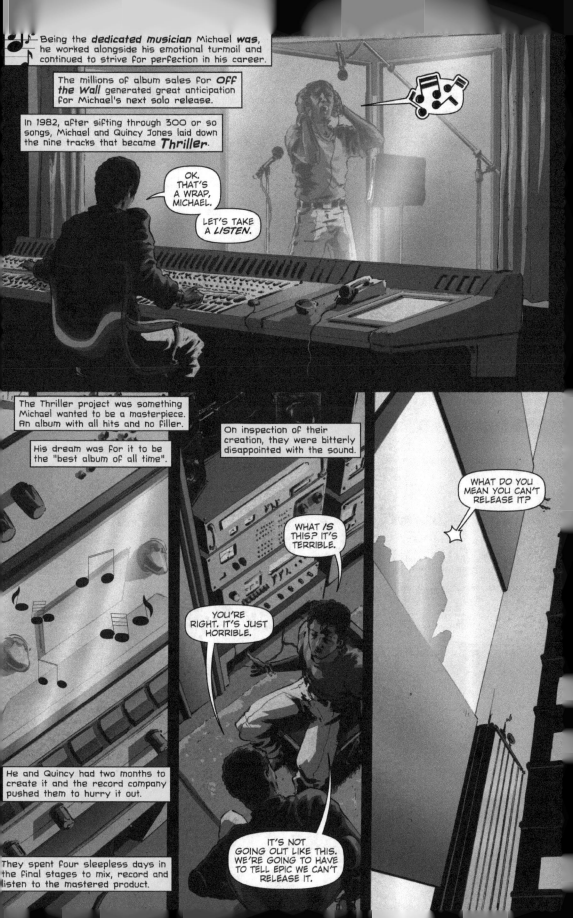

♪ Michael suffered second and third degree burns after a lighting effects flash bomb went off too close to his head.

While being treated for the accident, he visited many other burn victims and was moved by their stories.

So moved, in fact, that he donated a hyperbaric chamber and his $1.5 million settlement with Pepsi to the medical center's burn unit.

This kick started a string of charitable work that would begin to dominate his life outside of music.

That same year, Michael traveled with his brothers around the USA for their *Victory Tour*.

WOW! LOOK AT YOU GUYS. THERE'S SO MANY PEOPLE HERE.

THANK YOU ALL FOR COMING OUT TONIGHT.

WE ALL WANT YOU TO KNOW SOMETHING.

WE LOVE EACH AND EVERY *ONE* OF YOU!

WE LOVE YOU, *TOO*, MICHAEL!

His share of tour profits was given to charities-- all $5 million dollars.

It was a gesture well received by the public and media, some of whom had been skeptical about the large sums of money made by Michael and his brothers from their performances.

With the release of his next album *Bad*, in 1987, Michael set *another* record.

It became the only album to generate five number one hit singles.

It was quite a feat given that his previous release was already the best-selling album of all time.

Michael donated all his royalties from one of the hit tracks, *Man in the Mirror*, to the Camp Ronald McDonald Charity to help children with cancer.

The album's accompanying *Bad* tour was one of the most *successful* tours in history, with millions attending worldwide.

And although his schedule was hectic, he made sure to visit sick children at the hospitals in cities where he performed.

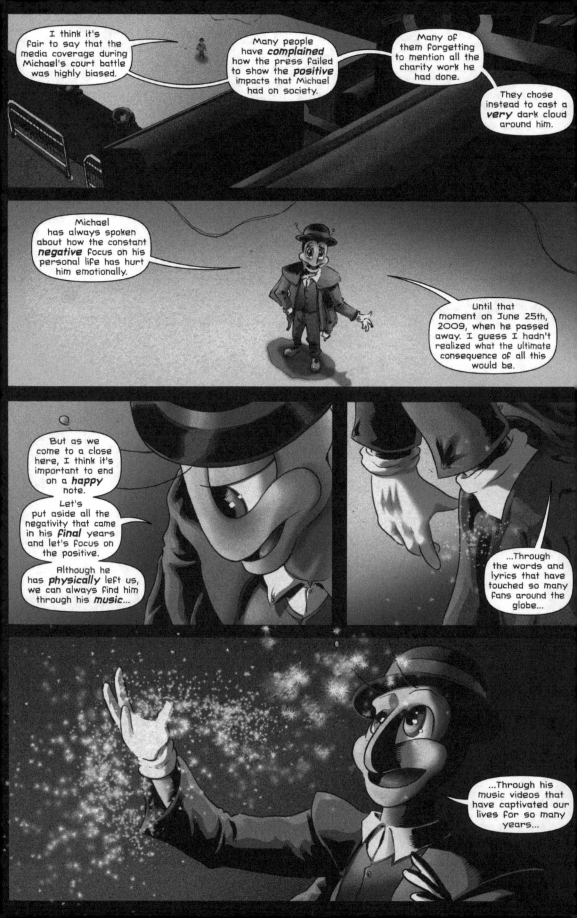

Mike Lynch, Michael L. Frizell, Michael Lent, Brian McCathy & Wei-Yuih Loh   Writer

Jayfri Hashim, Luis Chichon, George Amaru, Giovanni Timpano   Pencils

Benjamin Glibert & Warren Montgomery   Letters

Jayfri Hashim & Erick Marquez   Colors

Joe Phillips   Cover

Pin-ups: David Frizell

Darren G. Davis
Publisher

Maggie Jessup
Publicity

Susan Ferris
Entertainment Manager

CPSIA information can be obtained
at www.ICGtesting.com
Printed in the USA
LVHW061949310321
682943LV00023B/288